Baa Baa Black Sheep

Baa Baa Black Sheep

As told and illustrated by
Iza Trapani

WOOL FOR SALE

ISBN 978-1-58089-993-2

Published by Charlesbridge
85 Main Street
Watertown, MA 02472
(617) 926-0329
www.charlesbridge.com

Printed in China
10 9 8 7 6 5 4 3 2 1

For sweet Celia with love

Baa, baa, black sheep, have you any wool?
Yes sir, yes sir, three bags full.
One for the master, one for the dame,
One for the little boy who lives down the lane.
Baa, baa, black sheep, have you any wool?
Yes sir, yes sir, three bags full.

Baa, baa, black sheep, have you any milk?
Creamy, cold, and smooth as silk?
We spilled our milk—now what will we do?
Please fill our cups and we'll purr for you.

Goodness no, my shelves are very bare.
No sir, no sir, none in there.

Baa, baa, black sheep, have you any slop?
I've just finished my last drop.
I'll waste away if I don't eat soon.
One nibble ought to hold me till noon.

Silly pig, there is no slop in sight.
No sir, no sir, not one bite.

Baa, baa, black sheep, have you any hay?
Name your price and I will pay.
I'd like to buy two bales, maybe three.
I'll get the money—just wait and see.

No, I don't have any hay for sale.
No sir, no sir, not one bale.

Baa, baa, black sheep, have you any bones?
How my hungry belly groans.
Dogs cannot live on dry food alone.
Oh, won't you please just toss me a bone.

Heavens, no! I have no bones for you.
No sir, no sir, none to chew.

Baa, baa, black sheep, have you any seed?
Kindly help a friend in need.
Early this morning squirrels came by.
Knocked down my feeder, ate my supply.

No, I don't have any seed, my dear.
No sir, no sir, none in here.

Baa, baa, black sheep, have you any cheese?
May I have some pretty please?
Crackers taste yucky after a while,
A hunk of Swiss would sure make me smile.

No, I don't have cheese of any kind.
No sir, no sir, none you'll find.

Baa, baa, black sheep, won't you tell us why
"No" is always your reply?
A little kindness you've never shown.
Too mean to give a poor dog a bone.
Knit all day is all you ever do.
Boo, boo, black sheep, shame on you!

Baa, baa, black sheep, what a great surprise!
We can not believe our eyes.
We all assumed that you didn't care,
That you were selfish and wouldn't share.
Now we see and, wow, are we impressed!
You gave that which you give best!

Baa, baa, black sheep, have you any wool?
Yes sir, yes sir, three bags full.
When we have something special to give
We'll share with friends as long as we live.
Baa, baa, black sheep, have you any wool?
Yes sir, yes sir, three bags full.

Baa Baa Black Sheep

Baa, baa, black sheep, have you an-y wool? Yes sir, yes sir, three bags full.

One for the mas-ter, one for the dame, One for the lit-tle boy who lives down the lane.

Baa, baa, black sheep, have you an-y wool? Yes sir, yes sir, three bags full.

2. Baa, baa, black sheep, have you any milk?
   Creamy, cold, and smooth as silk?
   We spilled our milk—now what will we do?
   Please fill our cups and we'll purr for you.
   Goodness no, my shelves are very bare.
   No sir, no sir, none in there.

3. Baa, baa, black sheep, have you any slop?
   I've just finished my last drop.
   I'll waste away if I don't eat soon.
   One nibble ought to hold me till noon.
   Silly pig, there is no slop in sight.
   No sir, no sir, not one bite.

4. Baa, baa, black sheep, have you any hay?
   Name your price and I will pay.
   I'd like to buy two bales, maybe three.
   I'll get the money—just wait and see.
   No, I don't have any hay for sale.
   No sir, no sir, not one bale.

5. Baa, baa, black sheep, have you any bones?
   How my hungry belly groans.
   Dogs cannot live on dry food alone.
   Oh, won't you please just toss me a bone.
   Heavens, no! I have no bones for you.
   No sir, no sir, none to chew.

6. Baa, baa, black sheep, have you any seed?
   Kindly help a friend in need.
   Early this morning squirrels came by.
   Knocked down my feeder, ate my supply.
   No, I don't have any seed, my dear.
   No sir, no sir, none in here.

7. Baa, baa, black sheep, have you any cheese?
   May I have some pretty please?
   Crackers taste yucky after a while,
   A hunk of Swiss would sure make me smile.
   No, I don't have cheese of any kind.
   No sir, no sir, none you'll find.

8. Baa, baa, black sheep, won't you tell us why
   "No" is always your reply?
   A little kindness you've never shown.
   Too mean to give a poor dog a bone.
   Knit all day is all you ever do.
   Boo, boo, black sheep, shame on you!

9. Baa, baa, black sheep, what a great surprise!
   We can not believe our eyes.
   We all assumed that you didn't care,
   That you were selfish and wouldn't share.
   Now we see and, wow, are we impressed!
   You gave that which you give best!

10. Baa, baa, black sheep, have you any wool?
    Yes sir, yes sir, three bags full.
    When we have something special to give
    We'll share with friends as long as we live.
    Baa, baa, black sheep, have you any wool?
    Yes sir, yes sir, three bags full.

Froggie Went A-Courtin'

As told and illustrated by Iza Trapani

ıᴀı Charlesbridge

For Lou,
who helped to make
my dream come true

Froggie went a-courtin', he did ride,
H'hm, h'hm.
Froggie went a-courtin', he did ride
With a rose and chocolates by his side,
H'hm, h'hm.

Froggie said to Mousie, "Marry me,
Oh yes, oh yes.
Be my little honey, my sweet pea;
What a caring husband I will be,
Oh yes, oh yes."

"I don't want a frog to hold and squeeze,
Oh no, oh no.
I don't like the water, you hate cheese,
So you might as well get off your knees,
Oh no, oh no."

Froggie said to Turtle, "Be my bride,
A-ha, a-ha.
Hurry up my darling, do decide,
For a love like ours can't be denied,
A-ha, a-ha."

Turtle shook her head, "You move too fast,
Uh-uh, uh-uh.
We don't need an expert to forecast
That our marriage surely would not last,
Uh-uh, uh-uh."

Froggie said to Birdie, "Let us wed,
Oh please, oh please.
I will keep you happy and well fed.
Sweetie, make me proud and nod your head,
Oh please, oh please."

Birdie said, "I will not marry you,
No thanks, no thanks.
I would think about it if you flew,
But you smell of swamp; you're slimy too.
No thanks, no thanks."

Froggie said to Chipmunk, "Be my mate,
Yes ma'am, yes ma'am.
You and I should set a wedding date
And invite our friends to celebrate,
Yes ma'am, yes ma'am."

"Are you kidding me? Have you gone mad?
No sir, no sir.
I would never share your lily pad.
Just the thought of marriage makes me sad,
No sir, no sir."

Froggie saw a vision by the creek,
Oh my, oh my!
"Thump, thump" went his heart, his knees grew weak,
And his head did spin, he could not speak,
Oh my, oh my!

She said, "Froggie, will you marry me?
Yes yes, yes yes?
What a happy couple we will be.
I will cherish you, just wait and see.
Yes yes, yes yes!"

Froggie said, "My courtin' days are through."
Hooray! Hooray!
Joyfully he croaked, "I'll marry you!"
And they danced and hopped like froggies do!
Hooray! Hooray!

Froggie Went A-Courtin'

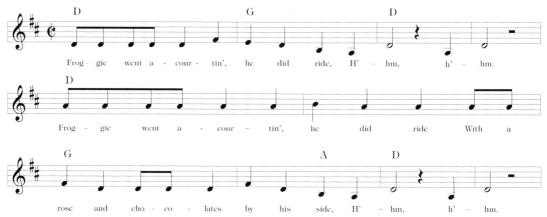

Frog - gie went a - cour - tin', he did ride, H' - hm, h' - hm.

Frog - gie went a - cour - tin', he did ride With a

rose and cho - co - lates by his side, H' - hm, h' - hm.

2. Froggie said to Mousie, "Marry me,
   Oh yes, oh yes.
   Be my little honey, my sweet pea;
   What a caring husband I will be,
   Oh yes, oh yes."

3. "I don't want a frog to hold and squeeze,
   Oh no, oh no.
   I don't like the water, you hate cheese,
   So you might as well get off your knees,
   Oh no, oh no."

4. Froggie said to Turtle, "Be my bride,
   A-ha, a-ha.
   Hurry up my darling do decide,
   For a love like ours can't be denied,
   A-ha, a-ha."

5. Turtle shook her head, "You move too fast,
   Uh-uh, uh-uh.
   We don't need an expert to forecast
   That our marriage surely would not last,
   Uh-uh, uh-uh."

6. Froggie said to Birdie, "Let us wed,
   Oh please, oh please.
   I will keep you happy and well fed.
   Sweetie, make me proud and nod your head,
   Oh please, oh please."

7. Birdie said, "I will not marry you,
   No thanks, no thanks.
   I would think about it if you flew,
   But you smell of swamp; you're slimy too.
   No thanks, no thanks."

8. Froggie said to Chipmunk, "Be my mate,
   Yes ma'am, yes ma'am.
   You and I should set a wedding date
   And invite our friends to celebrate,
   Yes ma'am, yes ma'am."

9. "Are you kidding me? Have you gone mad?
   No sir, no sir.
   I would never share your lily pad.
   Just the thought of marriage makes me sad.
   No sir, no sir."

10. Froggie saw a vision by the creek,
    Oh my, oh my!
    "Thump, thump" went his heart, his knees grew weak,
    And his head did spin, he could not speak,
    Oh my, oh my!

11. She said, "Froggie, will you marry me?
    Yes yes, yes yes?
    What a happy couple we will be.
    I will cherish you, just wait and see.
    Yes yes, yes yes!"

12. Froggie said, "My courtin' days are through."
    Hooray! Hooray!
    Joyfully he croaked, "I'll marry you!"
    And they danced and hopped like froggies do!
    Hooray! Hooray!

Here We Go 'Round the Mulberry Bush

As told and illustrated by Iza Trapani

For Ava Grace, who is everyone's sunshine!
With love, Iza

Here we go 'round the mulberry bush,
The mulberry bush, the mulberry bush.
Here we go 'round the mulberry bush,
So early in the morning.

Out of my garden—keep away!
Leave right now without delay.
Pests are not invited to stay,
So listen to my warning.

Oh, how I love to dig and hoe,
Scatter my seeds row by row,
Water them well and watch them grow
In spring when sunshine's glowing.

Oh, how we love to pull up roots,
Nibble on fresh and tender shoots,
Fill up on plump and juicy fruits,
In spring when plants are growing.

Didn't I say, "Do not return!"?
Those pesky critters have no concern.
I'll put up a fence and then they'll learn
I really mean good-bye.

In through the holes we slink inside.
Under the peas and lettuce we hide.
We're very teeny and can't be spied
While snacking on the sly.

Netting will surely do the trick.
I'll lay it on so nice and thick.
Stop those little skulkers quick
And make them go away.

Under the fence we tunnel through.
Broccoli! Beans! A dream come true!
Oh, how we love to chomp and chew
And gobble here all day.

I'll dig a trench that goes around,
Then add some fencing underground.
Send those gluttons homeward bound.
There's no way they'll get under.

Out in the field we leap and hop,
Up to the fence and over the top.
What a delicious bumper crop
To raid and loot and plunder!

This is my last and final try.
I'll build a fence that's really high.
Keep all those crooks from dropping by
And teach them to stay clear.

Open the gate, and we're in luck.
Corn on the cob, ready to pluck.
Oh, how we love to pick and shuck
All night when no one's here.

Here we go 'round the mulberry bush,
The mulberry bush, the mulberry bush.
Here we go 'round the mulberry bush.
'Round and 'round each year!

Here We Go 'Round the Mulberry Bush

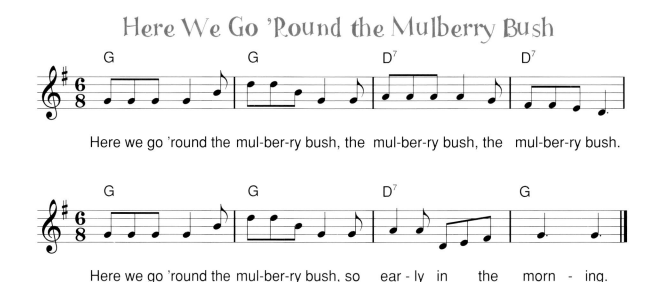

Here we go 'round the mul-ber-ry bush, the mul-ber-ry bush, the mul-ber-ry bush.

Here we go 'round the mul-ber-ry bush, so ear-ly in ___ the morn - ing.

Out of my garden—keep away!
Leave right now without delay.
Pests are not invited to stay,
So listen to my warning.

Oh, how I love to dig and hoe,
Scatter my seeds row by row,
Water them well and watch them grow
In spring when sunshine's glowing.

Oh, how we love to pull up roots,
Nibble on fresh and tender shoots,
Fill up on plump and juicy fruits,
In spring when plants are growing.

Didn't I say, "Do not return!"?
Those pesky critters have no concern.
I'll put up a fence and then they'll learn
I really mean good-bye.

In through the holes we slink inside.
Under the peas and lettuce we hide.
We're very teeny and can't be spied
While snacking on the sly.

Netting will surely do the trick.
I'll lay it on so nice and thick.
Stop those little skulkers quick
And make them go away.

Under the fence we tunnel through.
Broccoli! Beans! A dream come true!
Oh, how we love to chomp and chew
And gobble here all day.

I'll dig a trench that goes around,
Then add some fencing underground.
Send those gluttons homeward bound.
There's no way they'll get under.

Out in the field we leap and hop,
Up to the fence and over the top.
What a delicious bumper crop
To raid and loot and plunder!

This is my last and final try.
I'll build a fence that's really high.
Keep all those crooks from dropping by
And teach them to stay clear.

Open the gate, and we're in luck.
Corn on the cob, ready to pluck.
Oh, how we love to pick and shuck
All night when no one's here.

Here we go 'round the mulberry bush,
The mulberry bush, the mulberry bush.
Here we go 'round the mulberry bush.
'Round and 'round each year!

How Much Is That Doggie in the Window?

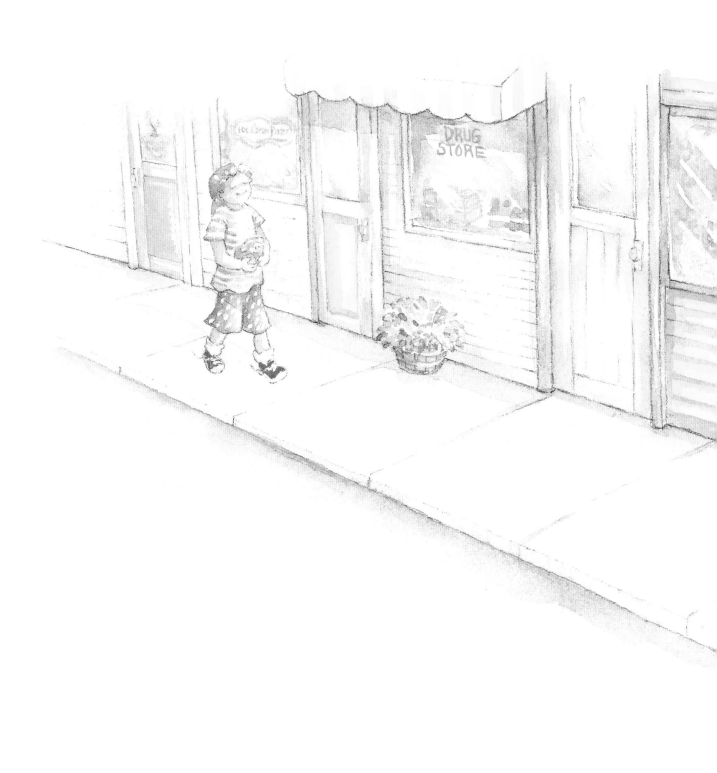

How Much Is That Doggie in the Window?

Words and Music by Bob Merrill

As retold and illustrated by

IZA TRAPANI

For Maciek and Kuba
with love
—I.T.

How much is that doggie in the window?
The one with the waggely tail.
How much is that doggie in the window?
I do hope that doggie's for sale.

That doggie's on sale for sixty dollars.
I'd even take five dollars off.
But you only have eleven fifty
I'm sorry, but that's not enough.

BIG SALE

DOG
FOR S
$ 6

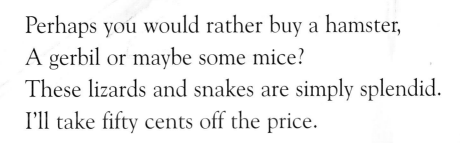

Perhaps you would rather buy a hamster,
A gerbil or maybe some mice?
These lizards and snakes are simply splendid.
I'll take fifty cents off the price.

Oh no mister, no, I want that doggie
Just look how he's wagging at me.
I'll go find a way to make some money
And I'll buy him, just wait and see.

I thought I'd sell lemonade on Monday—
Now that's a good plan, don't you think?
But it rained all day and most of Tuesday
And no one came out for a drink.

On Wednesday and Thursday I felt lousy—
I had a bad cold in my head.
The weather was great, but I was achy
And had to spend two days in bed.

On Friday my little baby sister
Fell down and she banged up her knee.
I went out and bought her frozen yogurt
And she was as pleased as could be.

On Saturday Mom was in the garden—
A bee stung her right on the toe.
I went out and bought her chocolate candy.
It made her feel better, you know.

On Sunday my Daddy got allergic.
He sneezed and his eyes itched real bad.
I went out and bought a box of tissues
And spent almost all that I had.

So that's why I didn't earn a penny.
I guess that I'm plain out of luck.
Last Monday I had eleven fifty
And now I have less than a buck.

Oh, where is that doggie in the window?
Oh, where did that cute doggie go?
I know that I can't afford to buy him.
I just thought I'd come say, "Hello."

Some people stopped in and bought that doggie
For their very special young son.
They bought him the dog so they could thank him
For all the nice things he had done.

Can that be the doggie from the window?
I wonder can that really be?
Oh, what a surprise! I never figured
That lucky young boy would be me.

How Much Is That Doggie in the Window?

How much is that dog - gie in the win - dow? The one with the wag - gel - y tail. How much is that dog - gie in the win - dow? I do hope that dog - gie's for sale.

2. That doggie's on sale for sixty dollars.
I'd even take five dollars off.
But you only have eleven fifty
I'm sorry, but that's not enough.

3. Perhaps you would rather buy a hamster,
A gerbil or maybe some mice?
These lizards and snakes are simply splendid.
I'll take fifty cents off the price.

4. Oh no mister, no, I want that doggie
Just look how he's wagging at me.
I'll go find a way to make some money
And I'll buy him, just wait and see.

5. I thought I'd sell lemonade on Monday—
Now that's a good plan, don't you think?
But it rained all day and most of Tuesday
And no one came out for a drink.

6. On Wednesday and Thursday I felt lousy—
I had a bad cold in my head.
The weather was great, but I was achy
And had to spend two days in bed.

7. On Friday my little baby sister
Fell down and she banged up her knee.
I went out and bought her frozen yogurt
And she was as pleased as could be.

8. On Saturday Mom was in the garden—
A bee stung her right on the toe.
I went out and bought her chocolate candy.
It made her feel better, you know.

9. On Sunday my Daddy got allergic.
He sneezed and his eyes itched real bad.
I went out and bought a box of tissues
And spent almost all that I had.

10. So that's why I didn't earn a penny.
I guess that I'm plain out of luck.
Last Monday I had eleven fifty
And now I have less than a buck.

11. Oh, where is that doggie in the window?
Oh, where did that cute doggie go?
I know that I can't afford to buy him.
I just thought I'd come say, "Hello."

12. Some people stopped in and bought that doggie
For their very special young son.
They bought him the dog so they could thank him
For all the nice things he had done.

13. Can that be the doggie from the window?
I wonder can that really be?
Oh, what a surprise! I never figured
That lucky young boy would be me.

THE
ITSY BITSY
SPIDER

The itsy bitsy spider
Climbed up the waterspout.

Down came the rain
And washed the spider out.

Out came the sun
And dried up all the rain,
And the itsy bitsy spider
Climbed up the spout again.

The itsy bitsy spider
Climbed up the kitchen wall.

Swoosh! went the fan
And made the spider fall.

Off went the fan.
No longer did it blow.
So the itsy bitsy spider
Back up the wall did go.

The itsy bitsy spider
Climbed up the yellow pail.

In came a mouse
And flicked her with his tail.

Down fell the spider.
The mouse ran out the door.
Then the itsy bitsy spider
Climbed up the pail once more.

The itsy bitsy spider
Climbed up the rocking chair.

Up jumped a cat
And knocked her in the air.

Down plopped the cat
And when he was asleep,
The itsy bitsy spider
Back up the chair did creep.

The itsy bitsy spider
Climbed up the maple tree.

She slipped on some dew
And landed next to me.

Out came the sun
And when the tree was dry,
The itsy bitsy spider
Gave it one more try.

The itsy bitsy spider
Climbed up without a stop.

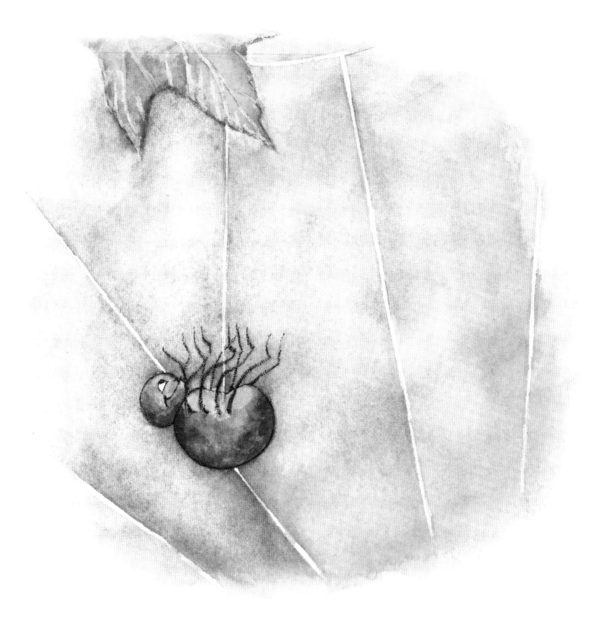

She spun a silky web
Right at the very top.

She wove and she spun
And when her web was done,

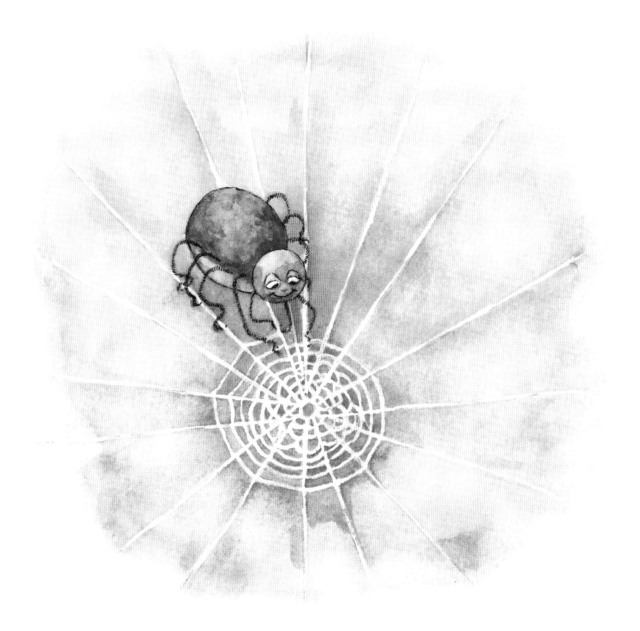

The itsy bitsy spider
Rested in the sun.

The it - sy bit - sy spi - der Climbed up the wa - ter - spout.

Down came the rain And washed the spi - der out.

Out came the sun And dried up all the rain, And the

it - sy bit - sy spi - der Climbed up the spout a - gain.

2. The itsy bitsy spider
Climbed up the kitchen wall.
Swoosh! went the fan
And made the spider fall.
Off went the fan.
No longer did it blow.
So the itsy bitsy spider
Back up the wall did go

3. The itsy bitsy spider
Climbed up the yellow pail.
In came a mouse
And flicked her with his tail.
Down fell the spider.
The mouse ran out the door.
Then the itsy bitsy spider
Climbed up the pail once more.

4. The itsy bitsy spider
Climbed up the rocking chair.
Up jumped a cat
And knocked her in the air.
Down plopped the cat
And when he was asleep,
The itsy bitsy spider
Back up the chair did creep.

5. The itsy bitsy spider
Climbed up the maple tree.
She slipped on some dew
And landed next to me.
Out came the sun
And when the tree was dry,
The itsy bitsy spider
Gave it one more try.

6. The itsy bitsy spider
Climbed up without a stop.
She spun a silky web
Right at the very top.
She wove and she spun
And when her web was done,
The itsy bitsy spider
Rested in the sun.

Mary had a Little Lamb

As told and illustrated by
Iza Trapani

For Rob and Gabe,
I love ewe with all my heart!

Mary had a little lamb.
Its fleece was white as snow,
And everywhere that Mary went
The lamb was sure to go.

And then one day the little lamb
Decided to be free,
And so it wandered off alone
To see what it could see.

Across the field, up to the barn
The little lamb did stray,
And there it met a big brown horse
And let it out to play.

But when the gate was opened up
The horse went charging out,
And in its dust the little lamb
Went stumbling all about.

It bumped into the tough old goose
As she was walking by.
She flapped her wings and hissed and pecked,
Which made the poor lamb cry.

The cow woke up and kicked a pail
Right up into the air,
And gave the lamb a milky bath
As it was standing there.

The little lamb raced back outside
Escaping, taking off,
But as it ran it tripped and fell
Into the water trough.

The lamb stood up and shook its fleece
But did not realize
The old barn cat would surely get
A very wet surprise.

The cat let out a shriek so loud,
It gave the hens a scare
And made them cluck and run around
In circles everywhere.

In the middle of this fuss,
A grumpy goat came by
And gave the lamb a mean old butt
Straight up into the sky.

Into the pigpen fell the lamb
And got completely stuck,
Then all the way from head to hoof
Was covered up in muck.

When Mary found her little lamb,
Its fleece was muddy brown.
She cleaned it up with lamb shampoo
And gently hosed it down.

She brushed and fed the little lamb
And kissed its sleepy head.
It looked at her with sheepish eyes
And then it went to bed.

Mary had a Little Lamb

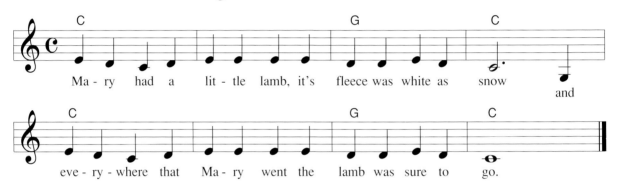

Ma - ry had a lit - tle lamb, it's fleece was white as snow and

eve - ry - where that Ma - ry went the lamb was sure to go.

2. And then one day the little lamb
   Decided to be free,
   And so it wandered off alone
   To see what it could see.

3. Across the field, up to the barn
   The little lamb did stray,
   And there it met a big brown horse
   And let it out to play.

4. But when the gate was opened up
   The horse went charging out,
   And in its dust the little lamb
   Went stumbling all about.

5. It bumped into the tough old goose
   As she was walking by.
   She flapped her wings and hissed and pecked,
   Which made the poor lamb cry.

6. The cow woke up and kicked a pail
   Right up into the air,
   And gave the lamb a milky bath
   As it was standing there.

7. The little lamb raced back outside
   Escaping, taking off,
   But as it ran it tripped and fell
   Into the water trough.

8. The lamb stood up and shook its fleece
   But did not realize
   The old barn cat would surely get
   A very wet surprise.

9. The cat let out a shriek so loud,
   It gave the hens a scare
   And made them cluck and run around
   In circles everywhere.

10. In the middle of this fuss,
    A grumpy goat came by
    And gave the lamb a mean old butt
    Straight up into the sky.

11. Into the pigpen fell the lamb
    And got completely stuck,
    Then all the way from head to hoof
    Was covered up in muck.

12. When Mary found her little lamb,
    Its fleece was muddy brown.
    She cleaned it up with lamb shampoo
    And gently hosed it down.

13. She brushed and fed the little lamb
    And kissed its sleepy head.
    It looked at her with sheepish eyes
    And then it went to bed.

Perhaps I shouldn't have scolded him when
He chewed a hole in my shoe.
But I had to teach my dog right from wrong.
What else was I going to do?

His feelings must have been terribly hurt.
His heart was filled with dismay.
So he packed his bowl and his favorite toy,
And then my dog ran away.

He took a bus that was headed for town.
A tourist, he thought he'd be.

But he never got past the rushing crowds,
And not one sight did he see.

"I think I'll go to the mountains," he said,
"And climb to my heart's content."
But he lost his grip on the icy slope.
Back down the mountain he went.

So next he thought he would surf in the sea.
He'd never tried it before.

But a giant wave knocked him off his feet,
And threw him back to the shore.

"I'd rather hike in the desert," he said.
"It's warm and peaceful out there."
But he tripped and fell on a rattlesnake.
It gave them both quite a scare!

"A cowboy's life is exciting," he'd heard.
"A rodeo could be fun."

But the horse he rode pitched him in the dirt.
My dog was glad to be done.

"I'm tired," he said. "I'll go to sleep in a cave.
How snug and cozy I'll be."
But he didn't know that a big brown bear
Would come keep him company.

By now my doggie was hungry and weak.
The sun was setting so low.
He longed to eat and he longed to sleep,
But had no place he could go.

And then he thought of his warm, loving home,
The place he most wished to be.
With a wagging tail and a joyful heart,
He ran right back home to me.

What great adventures my little dog had,
While roaming so far away.
Though he learned a lot and is wiser now,
I think he's come home to stay!

Oh where, oh where has my lit - tle dog gone? Oh where, oh where can he be?_____ With his ears cut short and his tail cut long, Oh where, oh where can he be?_____

2. Perhaps I shouldn't have scolded him when
He chewed a hole in my shoe.
But I had to teach my dog right from wrong.
What else was I going to do?

3. His feelings must have been terribly hurt.
His heart was filled with dismay.
So he packed his bowl and his favorite toy,
And then my dog ran away.

4. He took a bus that was headed for town.
A tourist, he thought he'd be.
But he never got past the rushing crowds,
And not one sight did he see.

5. "I think I'll go to the mountains," he said,
"And climb to my heart's content."
But he lost his grip on the icy slope.
Back down the mountain he went.

6. So next he thought he would surf in the sea.
He'd never tried it before.
But a giant wave knocked him off his feet,
And threw him back to the shore.

7. "I'd rather hike in the desert," he said.
"It's warm and peaceful out there."
But he tripped and fell on a rattlesnake.
It gave them both quite a scare!

8. "A cowboy's life is exciting," he'd heard.
"A rodeo could be fun."
But the horse he rode pitched him in the dirt.
My dog was glad to be done.

9. "I'm tired," he said. "I'll go sleep in a cave.
How snug and cozy I'll be."
But he didn't know that a big brown bear
Would come keep him company.

10. By now my doggie was hungry and weak.
The sun was setting so low.
He longed to eat and he longed to sleep,
But had no place he could go.

11. And then he thought of his warm, loving home,
The place he most wished to be.
With a wagging tail and a joyful heart,
He ran right back home to me.

12. What great adventures my little dog had,
While roaming so far away.
Though he learned a lot and is wiser now,
I think he's come home to stay!

Row Row Row Your Boat

Row row row your boat
Happy as can be
Sunshine glowing, off and rowing
With your family.

Row row row your boat
Stroke and follow through

Fumbling, flailing, oars go sailing—
What a clumsy crew!

Row row row your boat
Row with all your might

Rocking, bashing, water splashing
Better hold on tight!

Row row row your boat
Look ahead to find

Beavers damming, logging, jamming
Left you in a bind!

Row row row your boat
Stop to have a munch
Chomping, snacking, slurping, smacking
What a noisy bunch!

Row row row your boat
Better row to shore

Raining, hailing, wind is wailing
Hear the thunder roar!

Row row row your boat
Find a place that's dry
Scurry, scuttle, hide and huddle
Till the storm blows by.

Row row row your boat
And away you go

Skies are clearing, sunset nearing
Homeward bound you row.

Row Row Row Your Boat

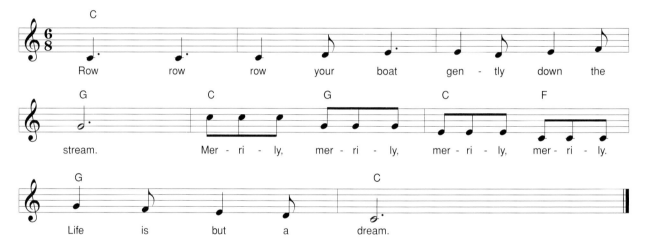

Row row row your boat gen – tly down the stream. Mer – ri – ly, mer – ri – ly, mer – ri – ly, mer – ri – ly. Life is but a dream.

2. Row row row your boat
   Happy as can be
   Sunshine glowing, off and rowing
   With your family.

3. Row row row your boat
   Stroke and follow through
   Fumbling, flailing, oars go sailing—
   What a clumsy crew!

4. Row row row your boat
   Row with all your might
   Rocking, bashing, water splashing
   Better hold on tight!

5. Row row row your boat
   Look ahead to find
   Beavers damming, logging, jamming
   Left you in a bind!

6. Row row row your boat
   Stop to have a munch
   Chomping, snacking, slurping, smacking
   What a noisy bunch!

7. Row row row your boat
   Better row to shore
   Raining, hailing, wind is wailing
   Hear the thunder roar!

8. Row row row your boat
   Find a place that's dry
   Scurry, scuttle, hide and huddle
   Till the storm blows by.

9. Row row row your boat
   And away you go
   Skies are clearing, sunset nearing
   Homeward bound you row.

That fly has gone away—
At last I'm free to play.
I told that pest to scram—
Now I'm happy as a clam.

Shoo fly don't bother me!
You're not my cup of tea.
Please stop annoying me—
Kindly go and let me be.

I think I'll find a nook,
Curl up and read a book.
Some nice and quiet spot—
Someplace where that fly is not.

Shoo fly don't bother me!
Go fly to Tennessee.
Leave on the count of three—
Can't you see you're bugging me?

I need to go outside
And find a place to hide.
My plan had better work,
Or I'll really go berserk.

Shoo fly don't bother me!
Please leave immediately.
Fly far away from me—
I don't want your company.

My tummy has a hunch
That it could use some lunch.
I think the coast is clear—
No more buzzing in my ear.

Shoo fly don't bother me!
Go find your family.
Go hide up in a tree.
Just don't stay and pester me!

I really need a rest
From that unwelcome guest.
I'd better take a nap;
Otherwise I think I'll snap.

Shoo fly don't bother me!
Go spread your wings and flee
Across the great blue sea,
All the way to Waikiki.

I'm beat without a doubt—
That fly has worn me out!
So now I'll close my eyes—
Hope that I don't dream of flies.

Shoo fly don't bother me,
Shoo fly don't bother me,
Shoo fly don't bother me—
I belong to somebody.

SHOO FLY!

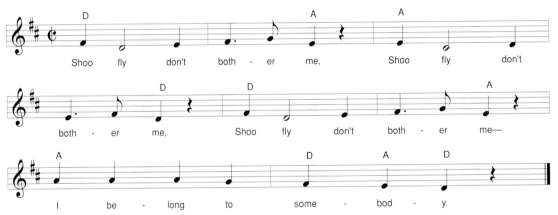

Shoo fly don't both-er me, Shoo fly don't both-er me, Shoo fly don't both-er me— I be-long to some-bod-y.

2. That fly has gone away—
At last I'm free to play.
I told that pest to scram—
Now I'm happy as a clam.

3. Shoo fly don't bother me!
You're not my cup of tea.
Please stop annoying me—
Kindly go and let me be.

4. I think I'll find a nook,
Curl up and read a book.
Some nice and quiet spot—
Someplace where that fly is not.

5. Shoo fly don't bother me!
Go fly to Tennessee.
Leave on the count of three—
Can't you see you're bugging me?

6. I need to go outside
And find a place to hide.
My plan had better work,
Or I'll really go berserk.

7. Shoo fly don't bother me!
Please leave immediately.
Fly far away from me—
I don't want your company.

8. My tummy has a hunch
That it could use some lunch.
I think the coast is clear—
No more buzzing in my ear.

9. Shoo fly don't bother me!
Go find your family.
Go hide up in a tree.
Just don't stay and pester me!

10. I really need a rest
From that unwelcome guest.
I'd better take a nap;
Otherwise I think I'll snap.

11. Shoo fly don't bother me!
Go spread your wings and flee
Across the great blue sea,
All the way to Waikiki.

12. I'm beat without a doubt—
That fly has worn me out!
So now I'll close my eyes—
Hope that I don't dream of flies.

13. Shoo fly don't bother me,
Shoo fly don't bother me,
Shoo fly don't bother me—
I belong to somebody.

Twinkle, Twinkle, Little Star

Twinkle, Twinkle, Little Star

As told and illustrated by

Iza Trapani

A special thanks to Anne Marie for opening the door,
and to Lou for letting me in.

For Aimee, Kyle, Rebecca, and Sophie—
some of the brightest little stars I know.

Twinkle, twinkle, little star,
How I wonder what you are!
Up above the world so high,
Like a diamond in the sky.
Twinkle, twinkle, little star,
How I wonder what you are.

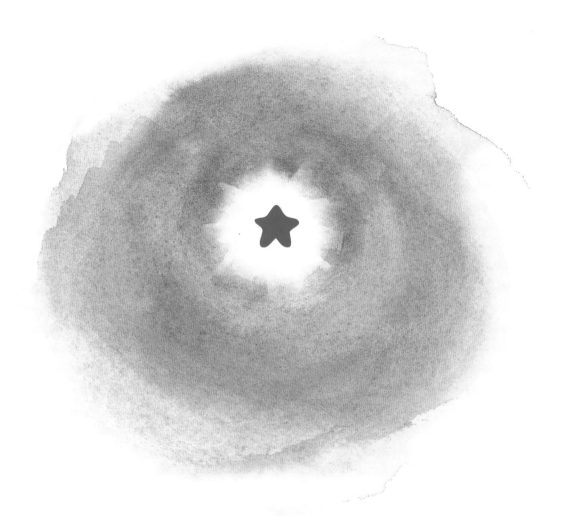

Twinkle, twinkle, star so bright,
Winking at me in the night.
How I wish that I could fly,
And visit you up in the sky.
I wish I may, I wish I might,
Have the wish I wish tonight.

Little child, your wish came true,
Here I am right next to you.
I'll take you on a magic ride,
So come with me—I'll be your guide.
There's so much that you'll see and do.
On this adventure made for you.

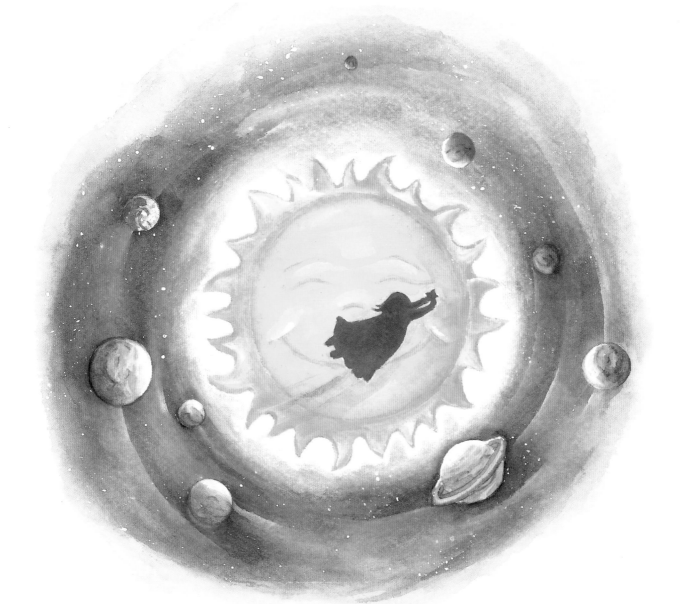

Look around you, little one,
There's the moon and there's the sun.
See the planets—count them all.
Some are big and some are small.
Can you name them one by one,
As they orbit 'round the sun?

Your planet Earth is such a sight,
I look at her with great delight.
When half the earth is in the sun,
The other half I glow upon.
For it's my job to twinkle bright,
On everyone who needs my light.

I shine on ships lost out at sea,
They know they can depend on me.
For even on the darkest nights,
I guide them to their harbor lights.
And lonely travelers wandering free,
Will find their way back home with me.

Everywhere I look below,
I shed my light and cast a glow.
Over cities, over farms,
On babies held in loving arms.
How I love to watch them grow,
As I shine on Earth below.

Little child, look down with me,
And tell me, tell me, what you see.
I see puppies in their bed,
A pony resting in his shed.
Little birds high in a tree,
And sleepy children just like me.

Yes, it's late—we can't pretend.
Our magic journey has to end.
I'll take you home, back to your bed,
You'll see me twinkling overhead.
But don't be sad—I do intend,
To shine on you each night, my friend.

Twinkle bright, my little star,
Watch me safely from afar.
Thank you for this magic night,
And the comfort of your light.
Twinkle, twinkle, little star,
What a special star you are!

Twinkle, Twinkle

Twin-kle, twin-kle, lit-tle star, How I won-der what you are!

Up a-bove the world so high, Like a dia-mond in the sky.

Twin-kle, twin-kle, lit-tle star, How I won-der what you are!

2. Twinkle, twinkle, star so bright,
    Winking at me in the night.
    How I wish that I could fly,
    And visit you up in the sky.
    I wish I may, I wish I might,
    Have the wish I wish tonight.

3. Little child, your wish came true,
    Here I am right next to you
    I'll take you on a magic ride,
    So come with me—I'll be your guide.
    There's so much you'll see and do,
    On this adventure made for you.

4. Out your window, through the sky,
    Up above the world we'll fly.
    Higher than a bird would go,
    To places only rockets know.
    Beyond the planes that soar up high,
    Is where we'll travel, you and 1.

5. Look around you, little one,
    There's the moon and there's the sun.
    See the planets—count them all,
    Some are big and some are small.
    Can you name them one by one,
    As they orbit 'round the sun?

6. Your planet Earth is such a sight,
    I look at her with great delight.
    When half the earth is in the sun,
    The other half I glow upon.
    For it's my job to twinkle bright,
    On everyone who needs my light.

7. I shine on ships lost out at sea,
    They know they can depend on me.
    For even on the darkest nights,
    I guide them to their harbor lights.
    And lonely travelers wandering free,
    Will find their way back home with me.

8. Everywhere I look below,
    I shed my light and cast a glow.
    Over cities, over farms,
    On babies held in loving arms.
    How I love to watch them grow,
    As I shine on Earth below.

9. Little child, look down with me,
    And tell me, tell me, what you see.
    I see puppies in their bed,
    A pony resting in his shed.
    Little birds high in a tree,
    And sleepy children just like me.

10. Yes, it's late—we can't pretend,
    Our magic journey has to end.
    I'll take you home, back to your bed,
    You'll see me twinkling overhead.
    But don't be sad—I do intend,
    To shine on you each night, my friend.

11. Twinkle bright, my little star,
    Watch me safely from afar.
    Thank you for this magic night,
    And the comfort of your light.
    Twinkle, twinkle, little star,
    What a special star you are!